The TAG, I'M IT!
Lenten Practice

An Invitation to Draw Closer to God through Thanksgiving, Acknowledgement, and Gratitude

Maureen Ryan Griffin

FLOATING LEAF PRESS

Author photograph by Donna Foster Photography
at www.donnafoster.com.

Published in the United States of America by

FLOATING LEAF PRESS

A division of

WordPlay

Maureen Ryan Griffin
6420 A-1 Rea Road, Suite 218, Charlotte, NC 28277
Email: info@wordplaynow.com
www.wordplaynow.com

ISBN 978-1-950499-00-7

For Kim Love Stump,
whose writing—and shining spirit—is always an inspiration.
Thank you for thinking up this book,
and for guiding it from start to finish.

PERMISSIONS

Thanks to Vecteezy.com for the use of the graphic that accompanies the daily quotes.

ACKNOWLEDGMENTS

Much gratitude to Kim Love Stump, Bridgett Bell Langson, and Wendy H. Gill for their creative insights and support, and to my longtime friend and life coach Nora McCormish, whose faith, love, and wisdom have often upheld me and have strengthened my own faith mightily. Special thanks to my entire class of Under Construction writers who served as a pilot group and provided valuable feedback: Amy Cole, Bridgett Bell Langson, Cindy Campbell, Cheryl Boyer, Jennifer Hurlbert, Kathy Brown, Kathy Gruhn, Kim Love Stump, Lisa Kunkleman, Mary Struble Deery, Rachelle McClintock, and T.D. Taegel, I know it is a cliché, but you truly do light up my life each week with your talent, heart, and generosity. I am ever grateful to my family and friends, especially my husband, Richard, whose love and steadiness is such ballast when my flights of fancy lift me too high aloft.

Welcome to the TAG, I'M IT! Lenten Practice

An Invitation to Draw Closer to God through Thanksgiving, Acknowledgement, and Gratitude

As you've learned from the back cover, the *TAG, I'M IT! Lenten Practice* is easy. Each evening (or as many evenings as you can), take a few quiet moments to reflect and write down three* "T's" (Things you're Thankful for), A's (Actions and Accomplishments you can Acknowledge yourself for, and "G's" (Gifts you're grateful for—in whatever form they took). The final step, (I'M IT!) is to choose three most-important-to-you actions you'll take the next day, based on how you hear God leading you, your deepest commitments, and what will inspire the most love, peace, and fulfillment.

*more are fine, but not needed

Why *three* "T's," "A's," "G's" and "I"M IT"s'?

Because three are enough to, over time, cause a profound change. Because, even on the fullest of days, three is do-able. It's also the number of the Trinity.

Why the evening?

Because *TAG, I'M IT!* is an uplifting way to end your day and promote peaceful rest, allowing you to settle your thoughts and emotions, claim the goodness in your life, and focus on what matters most to you rather than what may have disappointed, angered, or upset you.

Because all day long, you can think about what you'll write in your TAG. You'll find yourself noticing blessings large and small; gifts of kindness, empathy, time, talent, and treasure; synchronicities and serendipities that make you smile and feel God's presence. (Linda Matney, a dear friend of mine who is a spiritual powerhouse, call these "Godincidences.") Becoming present to these experiences is uplifting.

Full disclosure: Sometimes I'm so tired by the time my evening winds to a close that I save my *TAG, I'M IT!* for the following morning. It gets my day started off well, and still makes a huge difference in my walk with God.

An idea I love: I've taken to keeping my *TAG, I'M IT* journal with me so that, when I become aware of God's presence; feel thankful; accomplish something I feel good about; or receive a "gift," whether it's tangible or intangible, I can write it down right then. Not only am I guaranteeing that my loveliest moments won't be buried forever in the avalanche of tasks, interruptions, and distractions of my day, I'm also delighted when evening comes and my journal already has entries in it. The word *savor* comes to mind when I recall how this feels to me. Try this if it sounds good to you.

Now, here are some tips and ideas about each part of this journal so you can get the most out of it.

CLOSE-TO-GOD MOMENT

One of the women who tested out the year-long TAG, I'M IT practice noted that this process provides an invaluable record of the most noteworthy, grace-filled moments of one's days—a bonus benefit. And another suggested I add a spot to write out one single highlight per day. I loved this idea, and now find that this is my favorite part of the practice.

As I gathered one special moment each day, I recalled a wonderful poem by Joyce Sutphen called "The Book of Hours" in which she recounts beautiful hours in her life—like the hour, back in the seventies, she sat on a blanket in Central Park as Pete Seeger sang, "This Land Is Your Land," and the hour at a special art museum in a foreign country—and the hour in which she rescued a runaway dog from a busy road. She ends with the words, "that was an hour well/spent. Yes, that was a keeper."

One day, I realized that the highlight I chose to record was always one in which I felt especially close to God. Choosing a "closest moment" and sharing it with a group of fellow faith journeyers was a practice I'd learned years ago at a spiritual retreat. How good it has been to resume this habit!

What from your day is "a keeper"? In which moment did you feel especially enfolded by God's love? You can choose something included in your "TAG" lists, or a different experience.

When you leaf back through your *Tag, I'm It! Lenten Practice* journal, there it will be, kept safe for you to savor again.

TAG . . .

Think of the "TAG" part of this practice as a kind of gratitude "sandwich" that nourishes us bountifully. I have always loved the story in Exodus of how God provided manna to Moses and the Israelites in the desert, so I like to think of the goodness and gifts we receive and partake of daily as manna (bread) that we gather and are thankful for. And what is sandwiched between these abundant "slices" of God's grace at work in our lives? That filling is made up of our accomplishments and actions, both large and small, through which we contribute our gifts to the world, nourishing ourselves and others.

And why the inclusion of acknowledging ourselves for what we accomplish each day? This idea came about through a bit of WordPlay that came about when I noticed that *acknowledgment* has at its core the words *act* and *knowledge,* along with a suffix that denotes an action or resulting state. Aha! To acknowledge ourselves, I realized, is to give ourselves the knowledge that we have acted. Given I am so much more inclined to berate myself for what I DON'T accomplish rather than claim what I DO, I've found this shift heartening. The beauty of being present to what I accomplish through this list of completed "Ta-da's" (as opposed to as-yet-to-be-completed "To-do's) is that I now spend much more of my time mindfully doing what I can to further God's kingdom through my daily acts.

Following is a T-A-G breakdown, by letter.

Thanks-Giving

And now, our God, we give thanks to you and praise your glorious name.

1 Chronicles 29:13 (NRSV)

Thankfulness is a great energy that allows you to connect with your happiest, most creative self. Naming even a few of the good things in your life invites more good. It also lifts the heart, taps into positive emotion and provides solid, loving, nurturing ground to stand on each day.

Notice the good that you take completely for granted. (For example, I never offered thanks for having running water in our kitchen sink until it clogged and the plumber couldn't come for a few days.) Write down a good friend's name, the fact that there are people in the world who love you just as you are. Don't forget sensory delights: a Mary Poppins song, a cat's purr, a mockingbird trill. A crisp Winesap apple. The smell of rosemary rubbed between your fingers. Crisp, clean sheets. A dogwood in bloom. A photo that reminds you of a special trip and/or of someone you love.

Acknowledgement of Your Accomplishments and Actions

"Lord, now You are letting Your servant depart in peace,
According to Your word; . . ."

Luke 2:29 (NKJV)

Taking a few moments daily to acknowledge that I have tried to be a "good and faithful servant" allows me to feel a small sense of the peace expressed by Simeon, a "just and devout" man who was led by the Holy Spirit to come to the temple to see the Child Jesus, as "he took Him up in his arms and blessed God." (Luke 2: 28, NKJV)

What did you do today that made your corner of the world a little better? To whom did you offer a needed smile or a kindness? What useful end did you work toward, at work or at home? What healthy habits did you engage in? How did you add beauty and/or order to life? (Yes, even cleaning out your refrigerator or garage is, as my dad used to say, "a contribution to better living.")

As well as noting your service to others, give yourself "the knowledge that you have acted" on behalf of one of your own dreams or goals. And if you haven't, what could you do tomorrow? (You can make this an item on your "I'M IT!" list.) And don't forget that *how you're being* is as important as *what you're doing*. It's an accomplishment to be patient and cheerful when you feel like biting someone's head off!

Gratitude For Gifts Received

Every good and perfect gift is from above, coming down from the Father of the heavenly lights, who does not change like shifting shadows.

James 1:17 (NIV)

Yes, gifts are things we're thankful for. But there is a difference between Thanks-Giving for the good our "ordinary" lives hold and Gratitude for Gifts, which are, as they say in New Orleans, the "lagniappe" of life. Gifts can be physical objects, but can also come in the form of affirming words and experiences, kindnesses large and small, and serendipities and synchronicities that let us know God's divine love is guiding our lives. A parking spot close to the grocery store when it's raining is a gift. So is a compliment, whether it comes in a text, in an email, or in-person. So is finding the perfect gift for someone you love when you weren't even looking for it. The good news is that the more you pay attention, the more gifts you receive.

. . . I'M IT!

Then I said, "Here I am, I have come—
it is written about me in the scroll.
I desire to do your will, my God;
your law is within my heart."

Psalm 40:7-8 (NIV)

When it comes to serving God and others, crafting meaningful work, living a healthy lifestyle, building rewarding relationships, fulfilling our goals and dreams, each of us is IT! Yes, we all deserve rich support. But no one but you can determine how to best live out your vocation, which Frederick Buechner names as "where your greatest joy meets the world's greatest need." As choreographer Martha Graham said, "There is a vitality, a life force, an energy, a quickening that is translated through you into action, and because there is only one of you in all of time, this expression is unique. And if you block it, it will never exist through any other medium and it will be lost. The world will not have it. It is not your business to determine how good it is nor how valuable nor how it compares with other expressions. It is your business to keep it yours clearly and directly, to keep the channel open."

Each new day is an opportunity to listen as God speaks to us, to connect with the best within us, to mindfully choose what matters most. Yes, it takes courage to be the one to select, deliberately, only a few actions from the myriad of possibilities. But take heart. Take on being the one holding the reins of your life. Practice patience: some of our most desired outcomes can only be reached by taking one small step after another, and another . . . And much of our happiness comes from tending the love and beauty that is already ours. What three Important-to-You (and God) Actions will you take on day by day?

I hope this *TAG, I'M IT! Lenten Practice* adds joy and meaning to your days. One last tip: Invite a friend or family member to embark upon this process with you. Share with each other. You'll be spreading thankfulness and gratitude as you do, as well as adding to your own. As the apostle Paul urges in Hebrews 10: 24-25 ". . . let us consider how we may spur one another on toward love and good deeds, not giving up meeting together, as some are in the habit of doing, but encouraging one another—and all the more as you see the Day approaching." (NIV)

I am weak, but Thou art strong;
Jesus, keep me from all wrong;
I'll be satisfied as long
As I walk, let me walk close to Thee.

Just a closer walk with Thee,
Grant it, Jesus, is my plea,
Daily walking close to Thee,
Let it be, dear Lord, let it be.

~ American Traditional Spiritual

DAY 1: ASH WEDNESDAY

CLOSE-TO-GOD MOMENT:

T Thanks	A Acts	G Gifts

Rejoice always, pray continually,
give thanks in all circumstances;
for this is God's will for you
in Christ Jesus.

1 Thessalonians 5:16-18 (NIV)

I'm "It"

The three most-important-to-me things I will do tomorrow:

DAY 2: THURSDAY	*CLOSE-TO-GOD MOMENT:*	
T Thanks	**A** Acts	**G** Gifts

He has told you, O man, what is good;
And what does the Lord require of you
But to do justice, to love kindness,
And to walk humbly with your God?

Micah 6:8 (NASB)

I'm "It"

The three most-important-to-me things I will do tomorrow:

DAY 3: FRIDAY

CLOSE-TO-GOD MOMENT:

T
Thanks

A
Acts

G
Gifts

My brothers and sisters, whenever you face trials of any kind, consider it nothing but joy, because you know that the testing of your faith produces endurance; and let endurance have its full effect, so that you may be mature and complete, lacking in nothing.

James 1:2-4 (NRSV)

I'm "It"

The three most-important-to-me things I will do tomorrow:

DAY 4: SATURDAY

CLOSE-TO-GOD MOMENT:

T Thanks	A Acts	G Gifts

"Give thanks to the Lord,
for he is good;
his love endures forever."

Psalm 107: 1 (NIV)

I'm "It"

The three most-important-to-me things I will do tomorrow:

FIRST SUNDAY OF LENT

CLOSE-TO-GOD MOMENT:

T Thanks	A Acts	G Gifts

". . . the people living in darkness
have seen a great light;
on those living in the land
of the shadow of death
a light has dawned."

Matthew 4:16 (NIV)

I'm "It"

The three most-important-to-me things I will do tomorrow:

DAY 5: MONDAY

CLOSE-TO-GOD MOMENT:

T Thanks	A Acts	G Gifts

"You are the light of the world. A city set on a hill cannot be hidden; nor does anyone *light a lamp and put it under a basket, but on the lampstand, and it gives light to all who are in the house."*

Matthew 5:14-15 (NASB)

I'm "It"

The three most-important-to-me things I will do tomorrow:

DAY 6: TUESDAY	*CLOSE-TO-GOD MOMENT:*	
T Thanks	**A** Acts	**G** Gifts

"Let your light shine before men in such a way that they may see your good works, and glorify your Father who is in heaven."

Matthew 5:16 (NASB)

I'm "It"

The three most-important-to-me things I will do tomorrow:

DAY 7: WEDNESDAY

CLOSE-TO-GOD MOMENT:

T Thanks	A Acts	G Gifts

"Then you will be happy with the Almighty and look up toward God. You will pray to him, and he will listen to you, and you will keep your vow to him. When you promise to do something, you will succeed, and light will shine on your path."

Job 22:26-28 (GW)

I'm "It"

The three most-important-to-me things I will do tomorrow:

DAY 8: THURSDAY	*CLOSE-TO-GOD MOMENT:*	
T Thanks	**A** Acts	**G** Gifts

Then Jesus spoke to them again, saying, "I am the light of the world. He who follows Me shall not walk in darkness, but have the light of life."

John 8:12 (NKJV)

I'm "It"

The three most-important-to-me things I will do tomorrow:

DAY 9: FRIDAY

CLOSE-TO-GOD MOMENT:

T Thanks	A Acts	G Gifts

God is light; in him there is no darkness at all. If we claim to have fellowship with him and yet walk in the darkness, we lie and do not live out the truth. But if we walk in the light, as he is in the light, we have fellowship with one another, and the blood of Jesus, his Son, purifies us from all sin.

1 John 1:5b-7 (NIV)

I'm "It"

The three most-important-to-me things I will do tomorrow:

DAY 10: SATURDAY

CLOSE-TO-GOD MOMENT:

T Thanks	A Acts	G Gifts

Then your light will break through like the dawn,
and you will heal quickly.
Your righteousness will go ahead of you,
and the glory of the Lord will guard you from behind.

Isaiah 58:8 (GW)

I'm "It"

The three most-important-to-me things I will do tomorrow:

SECOND SUNDAY OF LENT	*CLOSE-TO-GOD MOMENT:*	
T Thanks	**A** Acts	**G** Gifts

He said to them, "But who do you say that I am?"

Simon Peter answered, "You are the Christ, the Son of the living God."

Matthew 16:15-16 (NKJV)

I'm "It"

The three most-important-to-me things I will do tomorrow:

DAY 11: MONDAY

CLOSE-TO-GOD MOMENT:

T
Thanks

A
Acts

G
Gifts

I will instruct you and teach you in the way you should go;

I will counsel you with my loving eye on you.

Psalm 32:8 (NIV)

I'm "It"

The three most-important-to-me things I will do tomorrow:

DAY 12: TUESDAY	*CLOSE-TO-GOD MOMENT:*	
T Thanks	**A** Acts	**G** Gifts

Be happy with the Lord,
and he will give you the desires
of your heart.
Entrust your ways to the Lord.
Trust him, and he will act on your behalf.
He will make your righteousness
shine like a light,
your just cause like the noonday sun.

Psalm 37:4-6 (GW)

I'm "It"

The three most-important-to-me things I will do tomorrow:

DAY 13: WEDNESDAY

CLOSE-TO-GOD MOMENT:

T
Thanks

A
Acts

G
Gifts

For where your treasure is, there will your heart be also.

Luke 12:34 (KJV)

I'm "It"

The three most-important-to-me things I will do tomorrow:

DAY 14: THURSDAY	*CLOSE-TO-GOD MOMENT:*	
T Thanks	**A** Acts	**G** Gifts

Wait for the Lord;
Be strong, and let your heart
take courage;
Yes, wait for the Lord.

Psalm 27:14 (NASB)

I'm "It"

The three most-important-to-me things I will do tomorrow:

DAY 15: FRIDAY

CLOSE-TO-GOD MOMENT:

T Thanks	A Acts	G Gifts

Be anxious for nothing, but in everything by prayer and supplication with thanksgiving let your requests be made known to God.

Philippians 4:6 (NASB)

I'm "It"

The three most-important-to-me things I will do tomorrow:

DAY 16: SATURDAY

CLOSE-TO-GOD MOMENT:

T Thanks	A Acts	G Gifts

. . . with all humility and gentleness, with patience, bearing with one another in love, making every effort to maintain the unity of the Spirit in the bond of peace.

Ephesians 4:2-3 (NRSV)

I'm "It"

The three most-important-to-me things I will do tomorrow:

THIRD SUNDAY OF LENT	*CLOSE-TO-GOD MOMENT:*	
T Thanks	**A** Acts	**G** Gifts

For where two or three are
gathered together in My name,
There I am in their midst.

Matthew 18:20 (NASB)

I'm "It"

The three most-important-to-me things I will do tomorrow:

DAY 17: MONDAY	*CLOSE-TO-GOD MOMENT:*	
T Thanks	**A** Acts	**G** Gifts

And the Word was made flesh, and dwelt among us, (and we beheld his glory, the glory as of the only begotten of the Father,) full of grace and truth.

John 1:14 (KJV)

I'm "It"

The three most-important-to-me things I will do tomorrow:

DAY 18: TUESDAY

CLOSE-TO-GOD MOMENT:

T Thanks	A Acts	G Gifts

So we have known and believe the love that God has for us.

God is love, and those who abide in love abide in God, and God abides in them.

1 John 4:16 (NRSV)

I'm "It"

The three most-important-to-me things I will do tomorrow:

DAY 19: WEDNESDAY

CLOSE-TO-GOD MOMENT:

T Thanks	A Acts	G Gifts

"Therefore do not worry, saying, 'What shall we eat?' or 'What shall we drink?' or 'What shall we wear?' . . . For your heavenly Father knows that you need all these things. But seek first the kingdom of God and His righteousness, and all these things shall be added to you."

Matthew 6:31-33 (NKJV)

I'm "It"

The three most-important-to-me things I will do tomorrow:

DAY 20: THURSDAY

CLOSE-TO-GOD MOMENT:

T
Thanks

A
Acts

G
Gifts

For the Lord is good; his mercy is everlasting; and his truth endureth to all generations.

Psalm 100:5 (KJV)

I'm "It"

The three most-important-to-me things I will do tomorrow:

DAY 21: FRIDAY	*CLOSE-TO-GOD MOMENT:*	
T Thanks	**A** Acts	**G** Gifts

But the fruit of the Spirit is love, joy, peace, patience, kindness, goodness, faithfulness, gentleness, self-control; against such things there is no law.

Galatians 5:22-23 (NASB)

I'm "It"

The three most-important-to-me things I will do tomorrow:

DAY 22: SATURDAY

CLOSE-TO-GOD MOMENT:

T
Thanks

A
Acts

G
Gifts

"Ask, and it will be given you; search, and you will find; knock, and the door will be opened for you. For everyone who asks receives, and everyone who searches finds, and for everyone who knocks, the door will be opened."

Matthew 7: 7-8 (NRSV)

I'm "It"

The three most-important-to-me things I will do tomorrow:

FOURTH SUNDAY OF LENT	*CLOSE-TO-GOD MOMENT:*	
T Thanks	A Acts	G Gifts

For now we see in a mirror, dimly, but then we will see face to face. Now I know only in part; then I will know fully, even as I have been fully known. And now faith, hope, and love abide, these three; and the greatest of these is love.

1 Corinthians 13: 12-13 (NRSV)

I'm "It"

The three most-important-to-me things I will do tomorrow:

DAY 23: MONDAY

CLOSE-TO-GOD MOMENT:

T
Thanks

A
Acts

G
Gifts

Yet I am always with you;
you hold me by my right hand.

Psalm 73:23 (NIV)

I'm "It"

The three most-important-to-me things I will do tomorrow:

DAY 24: TUESDAY	*CLOSE-TO-GOD MOMENT:*	
T Thanks	**A** Acts	**G** Gifts

"Commit to the Lord whatever you do, and he will establish your plans."

Proverbs 16:3 (NIV)

I'm "It"

The three most-important-to-me things I will do tomorrow:

DAY 25: WEDNESDAY

CLOSE-TO-GOD MOMENT:

T Thanks	A Acts	G Gifts

I know the plans that I have for you, declares the Lord. They are plans for peace and not disaster, plans to give you a future filled with hope.

Jeremiah 29:11 (GW)

I'm "It"

The three most-important-to-me things I will do tomorrow:

DAY 26: THURSDAY

CLOSE-TO-GOD MOMENT:

T Thanks	A Acts	G Gifts

Dear children, let us not love with words or speech but with actions and in truth. This is how we know that we belong to the truth and how we set our hearts at rest in his presence: If our hearts condemn us, we know that God is greater than our hearts, and he knows everything .

1 John 3:18-20 (NIV)

I'm "It"

The three most-important-to-me things I will do tomorrow:

DAY 27: FRIDAY

CLOSE-TO-GOD MOMENT:

T
Thanks

A
Acts

G
Gifts

Finally, brothers and sisters, whatever is true, whatever is noble, whatever is right, whatever is pure, whatever is lovely, whatever is admirable—if anything is excellent or praiseworthy—think about such things.

Philippians 4:8 (NIV)

I'm "It"

The three most-important-to-me things I will do tomorrow:

DAY 28: SATURDAY	*CLOSE-TO-GOD MOMENT:*	
T Thanks	**A** Acts	**G** Gifts

"Then I said, "Behold, I come;

In the scroll of the book it is written of me.

I delight to do Your will, O my God;

Your Law is within my heart."

Psalm 40:7-8 (NASB)

I'm "It"

The three most-important-to-me things I will do tomorrow:

FIFTH SUNDAY OF LENT

CLOSE-TO-GOD MOMENT:

T Thanks	A Acts	G Gifts

These things I have spoken to you so that My joy may be in you, and that your joy may be made full.

John 15:11 (NASB)

I'm "It"

The three most-important-to-me things I will do tomorrow:

DAY 29: MONDAY

CLOSE-TO-GOD MOMENT:

T Thanks	A Acts	G Gifts

The Lord is my shepherd,
I shall not want.

Psalm 23:1 (KJV)

I'm "It"

The three most-important-to-me things I will do tomorrow:

DAY 30: TUESDAY

CLOSE-TO-GOD MOMENT:

T
Thanks

A
Acts

G
Gifts

He maketh me to lie down in green pastures: he leadeth me beside the still waters.

Psalm 23:2 (KJV)

I'm "It"

The three most-important-to-me things I will do tomorrow:

DAY 31: WEDNESDAY

CLOSE-TO-GOD MOMENT:

T Thanks	A Acts	G Gifts

He restoreth my soul: he leadeth me in the paths of righteousness for his name's sake.

Psalm 23:3 (KJV)

I'm "It"

The three most-important-to-me things I will do tomorrow:

DAY 32: THURSDAY

CLOSE-TO-GOD MOMENT:

T Thanks	A Acts	G Gifts

Yea, though I walk through the valley of the shadow of death, I will fear no evil: for thou art with me; thy rod and thy staff they comfort me.

Psalm 23:4 (KJV)

I'm "It"

The three most-important-to-me things I will do tomorrow:

DAY 33: FRIDAY	*CLOSE-TO-GOD MOMENT:*	
T Thanks	**A** Acts	**G** Gifts

Thou preparest a table before me
in the presence of mine enemies:
thou anointest my head with oil;
my cup runneth over.

Psalm 23:5 (KJV)

I'm "It"

The three most-important-to-me things I will do tomorrow:

DAY 34: SATURDAY

CLOSE-TO-GOD MOMENT:

T Thanks	A Acts	G Gifts

Surely goodness and mercy shall follow me all the days of my life: and I will dwell in the house of the Lord for ever.

Psalm 23:6 (KJV)

I'm "It"

The three most-important-to-me things I will do tomorrow:

PALM SUNDAY	*CLOSE-TO-GOD MOMENT:*

T Thanks	A Acts	G Gifts

"I am the good shepherd. The good shepherd gives his life for the sheep."

John 10:11 (GW)

I'm "It"

The three most-important-to-me things I will do tomorrow:

DAY 35: MONDAY	*CLOSE-TO-GOD MOMENT:*	
T Thanks	**A** Acts	**G** Gifts

A new commandment I give to you, that you love one another; as I have loved you, that you also love one another.

John 13:34 (NKJV)

I'm "It"

The three most-important-to-me things I will do tomorrow:

DAY 36: TUESDAY	*CLOSE-TO-GOD MOMENT:*	
T Thanks	**A** Acts	**G** Gifts

The Lord may give you troubles and hardships. But your teacher will no longer be hidden from you. You will see your teacher with your own eyes. You will hear a voice behind you saying, "This is the way. Follow it, whether it turns to the right or to the left."

Isaiah 30:20-21 (GW)

I'm "It"

The three most-important-to-me things I will do tomorrow:

DAY 37: WEDNESDAY	*CLOSE-TO-GOD MOMENT:*	
T Thanks	**A** Acts	**G** Gifts

Therefore be imitators of God, as beloved children, and live in love, as Christ loved us and gave himself up for us, a fragrant offering and sacrifice to God.

Ephesians 5:1-2 (NRSV)

I'm "It"

The three most-important-to-me things I will do tomorrow:

DAY 38:
MAUNDY THURSDAY

CLOSE-TO-GOD MOMENT:

T Thanks	A Acts	G Gifts

Then he went away a second time and prayed, "Father, if this cup cannot be taken away unless I drink it, let your will be done."

Matthew 26:42 (GW)

I'm "It"

The three most-important-to-me things I will do tomorrow:

DAY 39:
GOOD FRIDAY

CLOSE-TO-GOD MOMENT:

T Thanks	A Acts	G Gifts

And when they had come to the place called Calvary, there they crucified Him, and the criminals, one on the right hand and the other on the left. Then Jesus said, "Father, forgive them, for they do not know what they do."

Luke 23:33-34a (NKJV)

I'm "It"

The three most-important-to-me things I will do tomorrow:

DAY 40: SATURDAY	*CLOSE-TO-GOD MOMENT:*	
T Thanks	**A** Acts	**G** Gifts

. . we receive the due reward of our deeds; but this Man has done nothing wrong." Then he said to Jesus, "Lord, remember me when You come into Your kingdom."

And Jesus said to him, "Assuredly, I say to you, today you will be with Me in Paradise."

Luke 23:41b-43 (NKJV)

I'm "It"

The three most-important-to-me things I will do tomorrow:

EASTER SUNDAY	*CLOSE-TO-GOD MOMENT:*

T	A	G
Thanks	Acts	Gifts

For God so loved the world that He gave His only begotten Son, that whoever believes in Him should not perish but have everlasting life.

John 3:16 (NIV)

I'm "It"

The three most-important-to-me things I will do tomorrow:

52528923R00035

Made in the USA
Columbia, SC
04 March 2019